We Just CLICked

A SIGNET BOOK

SIGNET

Published by the Penguin Group
Penguin Books Ltd, 27 Wrights Lane, London w8 5tz, England
Penguin Books USA Inc., 375 Hudson Street, New York, New York 10014, USA
Penguin Books Australia Ltd, Ringwood, Victoria, Australia
Penguin Books Canada Ltd, 10 Alcorn Avenue, Toronto, Ontario, Canada m4v 3b2
Penguin Books (NZ) Ltd, 182–190 Wairau Road, Auckland 10, New Zealand

Penguin Books Ltd, Registered Offices: Harmondsworth, Middlesex, England

First published 1995
1 3 5 7 9 10 8 6 4 2

For their kind permission to reprint part of *A Matter of Life and Death* from
Collected Poems by Anne Ridler the publishers acknowledge Carcanet Press Ltd
with gratitude.
The publishers have been unable to trace the copyright owner of the
untitled poem by E. Harris that appears on pages 64–7 and would be grateful
for any information that would permit them to give proper acknowledgement to
the poet and the publisher of the poem.

Illustrations taken from *Victorian Spot Illustrations, Alphabets and Ornaments from Porret's
Type Catalog: A Pictorial Archive of 1,460 Illustrations*, selected by Carol Belanger
Grafton (Dover Publications, Inc., New York, and Constable and Company,
London, 1982) and *Food and Drink: A Pictorial Archive from Nineteenth-century Sources*,
selected by Jim Harter, 3rd revised edition (Dover Publications, Inc., New York,
and Constable and Company, London, 1983)

Printed in England by Clays Ltd, St Ives plc
Set in 11/14.5pt Baskerville Monophoto

CLIC:
Cancer and Leukaemia in Childhood

The day you discover your child has cancer, your life changes for ever, but CLIC is there from the word go to offer love, practical help and real hope for the future.

It is vital that every child with cancer should have access to the best available treatment, so we pay for additional specialist doctors, nurses and other staff, both in hospitals and in the community, to make the ordeal of their treatment as straightforward as possible. And, very important, CLIC nurses and doctors have time, the most valuable commodity of all, to spend with these children and their families.

The disruption to normal life caused by a very sick child affects everyone – mums and dads, brothers and sisters, neighbours and friends. So CLIC helps out here too, with 'Homes from

Home' near the specialist cancer hospitals for families to stay in, 'crisis-break' flats for much needed short breaks away from it all and money to pay for that special holiday or an extra item for the home to make life a bit easier.

Ultimately, we all look towards a cure for these life-threatening diseases, and CLIC funds research into both the important new area of gene therapy as well as the causes of one of the most common childhood tumours.

CLIC relies entirely on the generosity of the public to fund this work, and your help will make a real difference – for example, £10 provides an

hour of CLIC nursing care for a dying child at home and £25 looks after a whole family for a weekend at a CLIC 'Home from Home'.

To make a donation of any size, or for more information, contact:

CLIC, 12/13 King Square, Bristol BS2 8JH. Telephone: 0117 9248844.

Introduction

Bob Woodward, the founder of CLIC (Cancer and Leukaemia in Childhood), is one of the most outstanding people I have ever met. Viewers of BBC TV's *Hearts of Gold* will have witnessed the presentation of the award to him and shared his joy in the creation of this book. It is designed to be the perfect gift for someone who loves or is loved – and at the same time it will raise desperately needed funds for this crucial charity.

As Bob Woodward himself says, 'It isn't the child who gets cancer – it's the whole family.'

Bob knew nothing of the world of the child with cancer until his eight-year-old son Robert was diagnosed and later died of the illness. In spite of this deep personal tragedy, Bob recognized that his family were fortunate. They had the advantage of local treatment near their home in Bristol.

For very many families the ordeal of looking after a sick child is harder. They travel long distances to spend days or weeks away from home in dreadful conditions. In some regions there isn't even a child-cancer specialist. This lack of specialist facilities, the sight of exhausted parents sleeping in hospital corridors, spurred Bob into action.

Two decades later CLIC has established self-catering 'Homes from Home', where the whole family can stay, free, during lengthy treatments at regional centres.

CLIC nurses care for children and families, helping from day one of diagnosis. They visit the child's home, become part of the family and ensure that each patient has as normal a childhood as possible. Routine treatments are carried out at home or even at school.

What began as one man's mission is now a huge, caring family that funds doctors, nurses, play therapists, researchers and a dedicated staff wonderfully supported by tireless volunteers and helpers. The royalties from this book will help fund CLIC nurses in their work for families across the UK.

I must thank all the distinguished and famous people who have supported CLIC and helped to create the book by sharing with us their own memories of romance and love. There are secrets in these pages that have never been revealed before and that I am sure you will enjoy sharing. Clearly, romance is alive and well in Britain today. Equally clearly, compassion and the love of children, epitomized by the work of CLIC, is a priority for you, our readers. Thank you for caring. We all hope you enjoy this very special book.

Esther Rantzen

We Just CLICked

....

Joss Ackland

....

I joined the company for the first Pitlochry Festival. The cast were all assembled for the first rehearsal, but I arrived late. A young girl with long, flowing hair crossed the room and sat down on a window sill, and I fell in love.

That evening she and I went to the theatre to see the Menotti opera *The Consul*. When we got to the box office I discovered I had no money, but Rosemary saved the day, and my self-respect,

by producing a traveller's cheque. Together we experienced the magic of a unique and wonderful show. Silently we shared the emotions touched off by the opera, saddened by the tragedy, elated by the music and joined in spirit, heart and mind. Silently we left the theatre and drank coffee together, and silently I saw her home to her digs near Regent's Park. Our joined hands unclasped when we reached her gate, and there, with a smile and quiet goodnight, we parted.

The next day I noted that Rosemary was wearing a ring. 'What is that?' I asked.

'An engagement ring,' she said.

'You're joking!'

'I'm serious.'

The bottom dropped out of my world. I went numb, my mouth was dry and I walked off in sulky anger.

From that moment there was a chasm between us. We felt confused and tormented – and we were to play the heroine and her lover Simon in J. M. Barrie's play *Mary Rose*.

But in rehearsal the play gradually took us over, the tension relaxed and we began to take long and frequent walks up the slopes of Ben Vrackie and to sit tranquilly by the mountain streams.

Eventually, the horn sounded and the walls of Jericho came tumbling down.

That was forty-three years, seven children and twenty-one grandchildren ago.

I can think of no better description of love than
these remarkable lines from Shakespeare's *Love's
Labour's Lost*, Act IV, scene iii.

But love, first learned in a lady's eyes,
Lives not alone immured in the brain,
But, with the motion of all elements,
Courses as swift as thought in every power,
And gives to every power a double power,
Above their functions and their offices.
It adds a precious seeing to the eye;
A lover's eyes will gaze an eagle blind;
A lover's ears will hear the lowest sound,
When the suspicious head of theft is stopp'd:
Love's feeling is more soft and sensible
Than are the tender horns of cockled snails:
Love's tongue proves dainty Bacchus gross in
    taste.
For valour, is not Love a Hercules,

Still climbing trees in the Hesperides?
Subtle as Sphinx; as sweet and musical
As bright Apollo's lute, strung with his hair;
And when Love speaks, the voice of all the gods
Makes heaven drowsy with the harmony.
Never durst poet touch a pen to write
Until his ink were temper'd with Love's sighs …

People often ask me, as they do other couples, how I met my wife. The short answer is that I walked into her bedroom!

I was eighteen years old at the time and had just joined the Royal Marines. Seven months later, the Commando Training Centre of Royal Marines in Lympstone, Devon, held its annual Christmas Ball. I didn't have a girlfriend, and neither did my best friend. But we invited our (female) cousins.

Being impoverished young officers, we put up our respective cousins in the cheapest pub we knew, which was the local that we frequented, just outside the Royal Marine Barracks.

When I turned up to see our friendly landlord, all dressed up for the ball in my Royal Marines mess kit (looking very dashing, I thought), I asked the publican which room my cousin was in, so that I could collect her. He obviously mistook which cousin belonged to whom and directed me to my friend's cousin, Jane Courtenay, so I burst into her room as she was in the process of dressing to go to the ball.

We married two years later!

Michael Aspel

This memory is special to me because it reminds me that the pain of love can strike with equal intensity at any time of one's life.

The first person
I was deeply in
love with (apart
from Deborah
Kerr) was
Margaret
Parnell, who
lived two streets
away from me
in Wandsworth.
I sent her an
anonymous note at
Sunday School, and she told me that when she
realized who had sent it, she nearly fainted.
Unfortunately, I discovered later that she really
fancied my best pal, Jim Healy.

Many years later I made a forlorn appeal on a
radio show: 'Margaret Parnell, where are you
now?'

The station received a swift message in reply:
'She's living in Carshalton, and she's married to
me, mate.'

Michael Barrymore

....

Candy Barrymore didn't make the biggest impact in the world the day she was born. Half Welsh and half dubious stock, she was the smallest of a litter of West Highland terriers. But her mother loved her as much as all the others, even though her tail curled the wrong way. At night in the kennel Candy's mum would hang her up by her tail for fear that she would be suffocated by the rest of the litter.

One thing that Candy became really good at was sleeping. She found it very easy. Close eyes, asleep. Open eyes, awake. She kept her eyes open as much as possible, and she really liked hanging

by her tail. She
became bored
with biting her
brothers' and
sisters' ears
and thought it
would be a
better idea to
do her favourite
thing: hang in the kennel and sleep.

When Candy next opened her eyes, she was aware of a strange quietness. Where was everyone? She went to the door of the kennel and nudged it with her nose. It was locked. Beads of sweat formed on the leather of her nose. For the first time in her young life, her tail curled the other way in dismay. Her family was gone. She pressed her face to the kennel door and drowsed.

What seemed like years, but was in fact just two days, passed by. Candy wondered if she would ever see her family again. As she thought, her face pressed up against the wire mesh in the door, a human being's foot placed itself beside her face. Her eyes opened wide. It was the biggest shoe she

had ever seen. The human being took off the shoe and left it by the kennel door. She heard a man's voice complaining that the shoe was hurting him. The end of the shoelace fell through the mesh of the kennel door. Candy, using her super-small brain, pulled and tugged the lace, made it into a perfect key shape and opened the door. With her unique curly tail
she covered
her tracks
and slipped
into the
bottom
of the
shoe.

The
human
being put the shoe back on and remarked on how much better it fitted. Candy lay low in the shoe for hours and wondered why it jumped around so much. And why, every time the shoe stopped jumping, she could hear people shouting and clapping.

It all became clear when the human being took off the shoe. She heard him say, 'There seems to be something in my shoe.' As he lifted the inner sole to examine it, Candy caught sight of him. To this day she doesn't know why, but when she looked into his eyes her tail curled the right way.

Michael and Candy Barrymore have been living together since then and have no children!

David Bellamy

We were both teenagers between school and university. I saw Rosemary, in her school uniform,
deliver the Christmas post in Springclose Lane,
Cheam, Surrey.

We fell in love and still love each other, forty-one
Christmases on.

Cilla Black

February brings a day for choosing,
Like a singer needs a song.
We all need understanding,
Like a padlock needs a key.
Love is the power
To set us free.
Cupid's arrow knows no boundaries,
Like a picture needs a hook.
Love's artist needs no canvas,
Like a husband needs a wife.
We got lucky:
We just CLICked.

Mr Blobby

....

I am often asked how I first met Mrs Blobby. All I can say is … I'm still recuperating. We didn't so much 'CLICk' as 'galumph'! And when they talk of 'falling in love' – well, we did that too, over and over and over and over again!

It was midnight in Crinkley Bottom,
and nightingales sang Pink Floyd,
and right over there,
across the still square –
a silhouette you couldn't avoid.

From out of a darkened corner
a woman emerged, so big.
My confusion dissolved
when her eyeballs revolved
and it was clear she was wearing a wig.

She approached me
   quite gently and kindly
but my legs were all wobbly and dithered.
She walked forward a pace –
looked right into my face –
and stood on my foot, so I withered.

I asked her her name, and a whisper there came,
and both my eyes started aglowing.
The word I had heard
sounded so much like 'nerd'
that I thought it was time I was going.

She chased me until I was panting,
past where Pru's woollen shop had been.
Then at Sammy's old house
she cried: 'I'm your spouse!'
I thought: 'His windows could do with a clean.'

The light was much better – her face I could see,
and a moment to treasure was had.
So beneath the oak tree
I went down on one knee
and invited her back to my pad.

Her attractions and virtues are many –
too many to disclose in this ode.
But what I will say
is that on a clear day
you can see through her head down the road.

And our tums are as big as each other's:
we enjoy the same zest for life.
But I'd never have guessed,
in my long, lonely quest,
I'd love someone like me for a wife.

What followed is history – a legend of sorts:
The rest of the tale is too sloppy.
But as our love's grown
we're more commonly known
as Mr and Mrs Blobby.

Ian Botham

The year: 1972. The venue: Weston-super-Mare. The occasion: a cricket game, Somerset v. Northamptonshire. I was sitting on the veranda of the Old Pavilion talking to one or two of the older Somerset players. A girl walked by, deep in conversation with an older couple and a younger girl. She was wearing a multi-coloured polo sweater, navy hot pants and long white boots (very fashionable in the early 1970s), and her hair was caught back in a pony tail. For a moment the conversation ceased, then the silence was broken

when I said something to the tune of 'She's a bit of all right – wouldn't mind taking her out.'

The girl disappeared, never to be seen again – so I thought. We met again several years later and are soon to celebrate our nineteenth wedding anniversary. Gerry and Jan, Kath's parents, celebrated their ruby anniversary last year, as had my parents, Les and Marie, a few years earlier. The younger girl I saw with Kath all those years ago is my sister-in-law Lindsay.

I certainly impressed Kath with my recollection of that first 'meeting', although she still cringes at the thought of the polo sweater, hot pants and long white boots. They impressed me – but I'm glad the hairstyle has changed!

I once had a row with a boyfriend I was mad about. He refused to see me, and I looked all over town for him, ending up at his best friend's house, crying my eyes out for two hours after bemoaning my fate – only to discover, the next day, that he had been hiding in the wardrobe in his friend's room listening to it all.

I wasn't quite so keen after that.

Ken Bruce

A Scots romantic
may seem a
contradiction in
terms, but I find
we're represented
perfectly by the
great Robert
Burns: his words
are simple, robust,
straightforward
and effective.

Come let me take thee to my breast,
And pledge we ne'er shall sunder,
And I shall spurn as vilest dust
The world's wealth and grandeur!

Barbara Cartland

So Long A Time

Is it twenty years since you said goodbye?
I remember your roses made me cry.
And your letter which said so little and yet
I knew it was something I'd never forget.

Twenty years and I can still hear
That note in your voice when our lips were near,
The feel of your arms, your mouth, your hands
That encompass me still like unbreakable bands.

I laugh, seem busy and people say,
'It's wonderful how you are always gay,'
But when I think of you now I know
Those twenty years have been slow ...
    slow ... slow.

This was written many years ago. He was fair,
blue-eyed and very charming. It should have
been so perfect, but a quirk of fate decreed otherwise – fate that strange, mysterious power against
which there is no appeal.

John Cole

....

I found my wife at an international football match. At the time I was a newspaper reporter in Belfast, not knowledgeable enough about football to cover the match but allowed to be there — which was what I wanted — so long as I wrote a piece about the 'pre-match entertainment'.

This was organized by the Central Council for Physical Education and consisted of a group of PE teachers — or 'gym mistresses', as we called them in those unreconstructed times — performing Scottish and other country dances. They were not only in short skirts but also barefooted, dancing on the green grass of Windsor Park, where our heroes would soon be doing battle with Scotland (though not in their bare feet).

In 1954, the lads on Spion Kop had never seen anything more erotic, and there was much wolf-whistling. The dancers, whom I encountered under the grandstand afterwards, were flattered, though a little flustered, by this attention. I struck while the iron was hot, and the feet cold, and arranged my first date with Madge, my wife.

Richard Coles

Love and the Poet

Love inspires the poet to verses
(the lucky to paeans, the jilted to curses).
From time immemorial numberless suitors
Have taken up quills, pens and laptop computers
And fashioned such verse as their talent permitted,
For which they are lauded, ignored or committed.
Yet, skilful or awful, it is my endeavour
To trump all their efforts by crafting with cunning
    and bland disregard for poetic propriety a last
    line so long and so artlessly prolix that, while
    overlooked by the Guardians of Poesy, it may be
    considered to be a contender for Worst Last
    Line Written by Amateur Wordsmith.
Ever.

I theng yew.

Brian Conley

Love is very special to me because I always remember the first time I fell in love.

I was on holiday in Spain, and I met this girl in the hotel swimming pool. I took her out a few times, but she kept jumping back in. She was gorgeous. She had jet-blond hair, and I loved her for what she was ... rich!

One evening we say beneath a starlit sky. The Mediterranean glistened in the moonlight. We were young and in love.

I drank champagne

from her slipper. It held two pints! I nearly choked on the cornpads.

Back at the hotel we lingered over a candlelit dinner, won a fortune at the casino and finally walked, hand in hand, along the beach.

The next day I was inspired to write this poem:

Last night I held a little hand
so dainty and so sweet
I thought my heart would surely break
so wildly did it beat.
No other hand in all the world
can greater comfort bring
than the hand I held last night –
four aces and a king!

Robin Cousins

The first time we met she was terribly cold,
not nice and inviting, but scratched up and old.
But she gradually worked her great magic spell,
and our relationship grew, as my poem will tell.

After just a few months we were seen as a team,
the envy of many (our moves they had seen).
We were together a lot, each day more and more –
I would eat, drink, and sleep her like never before.

All over the world she and I would be seen
in public, in private, on the television screen.
Over twenty years now and we're still best of friends:
with luck, it'll be years before our relationship ends.

In fact, we're a threesome. It's really quite nice –
Just me and my skates and a lady called Ice.

Leslie Crowther

With Jean and me it was love at first sight – or, rather, with me it was lust at first sight. You see, Jean was wearing a leotard, and I swear to you I had never seen anything so provocative! She was queuing, quite harmlessly, in the restaurant that Knifeman Schools provided for the nourishment of their students – Jean was in the Ballet section and I was in the Drama section.

We were to meet later on, in the Festival year of 1951, when Robert Atkins decided that he would mount *A Midsummer Night's Dream* as the Open-air Theatre, Regent's Park, contribution to the Festival. I played the part of Flute, the bellows mender (one of the 'rude mechanicals'), and Jean was leading the fairies in the ballet chorus. Now, round about this time I had evolved a ruse that never failed. Putting on a love-sick air, I would gaze into the eyes of whichever bird I had decided to pull and duly trot out Shakespeare's love sonnet 'Shall I compare thee to a summer's day?' Sometimes it worked, sometimes it didn't. The one time it most assuredly didn't was when a beautiful ballet dancer confided to Jean that she thought I recited Shakespeare's verse very well.

'Oh, does he?' was Jean's steely reply. You see, I'd played the same trick with Jean in the bushes behind the stage only half an hour before. (I really must keep a diary.)

Only by dint of passionate wooing was I able to put *that* one right. But put it right I did, and the upshot of it was that we celebrated our ruby wedding this year. And if it weren't for the caring of my Florence (Jean) Nightingale, I wouldn't have recovered sufficiently to take on my current workload.

Paul Daniels

....

As everyone knows, I am not only a great romantic but also, arguably, England's finest sex symbol
– but it was not always so. In fact, as a shy and
sickly youth I had no idea what happened to
noses when you kissed. I mean, when you kiss,
where does the nose
go? This was the
question that filled
my mind during my
early years, and I had
a vague idea that the
same thing would
happen to my nose
as occasionally hap-
pened to me on the
pavement outside the
terraced house where
we lived.

You know the feeling; you walk up the road and you meet somebody. As you step to the left, they step to the right; as they step to the left, you step to the right, and you both go backwards and forwards, not being able to pass each other. I was frightened to kiss a girl in case this happened to my nose. Would my nose turn to the left as hers turned to the right? I used to feel my cheeks to see if there was a socket in them where her nose would fit so that our lips could meet.

One fateful evening, however, Wendy and I wandered into a back alley behind Munby Street, in South Bank near Middlesbrough, and she looked expectantly at me and I knew the moment had come. Our lips approached each other and – yes, you've guessed it – my nose turned to the left, hers to the right, and our heads weaved backwards and forwards in the flickering street lights. Finally, I grabbed her head, bent it to the right, turned mine to the left and kissed her. I felt nothing at all other than puzzlement and wondered why people did this instead of card tricks. Times have changed.

Antonia de Sancha

....

I believe that in life you only ever have one true love, and, no matter what happens, that love will remain in your heart throughout. My husband is my true love. We met purely by chance through a mutual friends of ours. He invited me out for a curry and a beer, which I couldn't resist, and from that moment we saw each other every day, which gradually led to my falling in love with him.

I now know there is nothing more important in life than having another half. Falling in love with my husband has made me feel what it is to be truly happy.

I'm a very lucky woman.

Judi Dench

....

Shakespeare's Sonnet 116

Let me not to the marriage of true minds
Admit impediments. Love is not love
Which alters when it alteration finds,
Or bends with the remover to remove:
O, no! it is an ever-fixèd mark,
That looks on tempests and is never shaken;
It is the star to every wand'ring bark,
Whose worth's unknown, although his height be
    taken.
Love's not Time's fool, though rosy lips and
    cheeks
Within his bending sickle's compass come;
Love alters not with his brief hours and weeks,
But bears it out even to the edge of doom.
If this be error, and upon me prov'd,
I never writ, nor no man ever lov'd.

Sacha Distel

....

When I was six years old I fell in love (madly!) for the first time.

I was at school (in the third year) and she was … the teacher.

And — would you believe it? — her name was VALENTINE.

Paul Eddington

The year was 1949. The day was the first one of the season at the old Playhouse, the Sheffield Repertory Theatre. I was awaiting the arrival of new members of the company. An enchanting girl, tall and slim with dark hair and dark eyes, came up the steps and into the darkened wings.

As I greeted her she told me her name was Patricia Scott and that she had come from the Bristol Old Vic Theatre School. 'That's the girl for me,' I thought.

We have been married now for nearly forty-three years.

Michael Fish

What I felt at the sight of my first child being born, hearing her very first cry and seeing the look on my wife's face as she asked for the Sunday papers and a cup of tea was, for me, love.

I will never forget the pain I went through as my hand was squeezed to pulp or the joy and pride I felt when I held my daughter for the very first time.

Nor will I forget being asked by the junior doctor, just after the birth, 'What do we do next?'

Brian Glover

Ladies' choice

She stood up, fluffed up her taffeta skirt, stuck out her courting tackle and headed straight across the floor like an Exocet missile – if they'd had Exocet missiles in the days when they still had ladies' choice.

In those days you still had rules, especially in dance halls, and ladies' choice meant exactly

what it said; if a lady wished to dance with a gentleman, it was up to her to ask him, and only a lady could excuse during ladies' choice.

'She's got a bloke,' my mate whispered.

'I've got a brand-new pair of green suede shoes.' I really fancied myself in those shoes. 'And I've CLICked.'

'And he props for Trinity.'

I'm not sure if it was the new green suede shoes or coming from Barnsley that failed to alert me to the significance of the warning. Wakefield to Barnsley is only ten miles, but it's another world, another culture. Barnsley's football: Wakefield's rugby league. Plus I was young. Impetuous. She was beautiful. Could have pulled ducks off water. And now she was standing in front of me, court-ing tackle heaving.

'Are you getting up?'

I was already up. We never sat down. The lasses sat down: the lads stood up. It was one of the rules. And another rule was that a gentleman could not refuse a lady.

Slow, slow, quick, quick, slow. We hadn't completed one circuit when I felt this tap on my shoulder.

He hadn't got a head, just a neck with a face in it. I asked him what he wanted. No reply. Just stood there, making sure I could see the Wakefield Trinity badge on his blazer. I inquired again what he wanted. Still no reply, so I pulled her back into my arms, and off we glided. Slow, slow, quick, quick, slow.

This time it wasn't a tap. It was a definite prod.

I hoped he wasn't deaf as well as daft. 'It's ladies' choice. A gentleman can't excuse. Not when it's ladies' choice. Only a lady can … '

I was rudely interrupted.

I'll tell you something for nothing; it's virtually impossible to get bloodstains out of green suede.

Julie Goodyear

I wish I still had a mother,
Especially one like mine.
She thought the sun shone out of me,
Yet she made my sun shine.

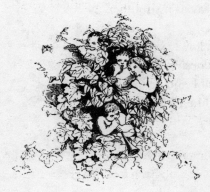

To her I was an angel,
A daughter she'd not change.
If anyone said otherwise,
She thought of them as strange.

The day she died I lost a friend
And failed to find another,
For somehow no one saw me
In the same way as my mother.

The long and lonely years have passed,
The sadness doesn't end,
And never will I find again
Such love within a friend.

This poem was given to me by
a friend shortly after the death of
my mother. It did, and still does, mean a great
deal to me because me and my mum just
CLICked.

Jilly Goolden

....

Taken from *A Matter of Life and Death* in *Collected Poems* by Anne Ridler, Carcanet Press Ltd, 1994

I did not see the Iris move,
I did not feel the unfurling of my love.

This was the sequence of the flower:
first the leaf from which the bulb would swell,
no prison, but a cell,
a rolled rainbow;
then the sheath that enclosed the blow
pale and close,
giving no hint of the blaze within,
a tender skin with violet vein.
Then the first unfurling petal,
as if a hand that held a jewel
curled back a finger, let the light wink

narrowly through the chink,
or like the rays before the sunrise
promising glory.

And while my back is turned, the flower has blown.
Impossible to tell
how the opulent blossom from that spick bud has
    grown.
The chrysalis curled tight,
the flower poised for flight –
corolla with lolling porphyry wings
and yellow tiger markings
a chasing-place for shade and light:
between these two, the explosion
soundless, with no duration.

(I did not see the Iris move,
I did not feel my love unfurl.)

The most tremendous change takes place in
    silence,
unseen, however you mark the sequence,
unheard, whatever the din of exploding stars.

I fell in love with this poem when I heard it read
by the author and when, a few months later, I fell
in love with Paul, my husband, I gave it to him
(it's published in a slim volume on its own). It was
only when we had our first child a year after that
that we came to our senses and realized the
poem, in fact, celebrates the greatest love of all:
the love you feel on the birth of a child.

Sally Gunnell

....

It was on a Junior International Athletic trip to Australia.

I remember noticing Jon Bigg on the aircraft on the outward flight. He was one of only two guys wearing shorts – everyone else had a tracksuit on – and he walked around, smiled a lot and seemed to know many people. I knew I had seen him before, during one of our weekend get-togethers up in Gateshead maybe a year or two earlier. There, as on the plane, he seemed friendly and self-confident, grinning at everyone. I thought, 'Oh, he's quite nice!'

We stayed at a university in Melbourne, and Jon was always around, part of the group, chatting away. I hit it off with him from the word go. He was so easy to get on with, and he blended in with us all as if he were a friend we had known for years. I remember sitting quite close to him during dinner in the immense dining hall in the university, and afterwards, during the rest of the three-week trip, we were usually together, hanging out in a loosely defined group of about half a dozen. Some days we would go down to the beach or train together or go swimming. Sometimes it was the whole group, and at other times it would be just the two of us. Nothing binding was said or expected; no commitments were made.

Yes, I definitely fancied him, but I wasn't about to rush into anything. We were just getting to know each other. This set a pattern that was to continue for several more months. Gradually, Jon and I grew a little closer ... It seemed that our interests and our humour just CLICked!

After I had won my Olympic Gold Medal, we were married on 19 October 1992 during an open-air ceremony on a quiet beach on the Gulf of Mexico.

David Jacobs

I must have been a very backward lad, for I didn't receive my first real kiss until I was fifteen. I was staying with relatives in the country to escape the Blitz, and their Austrian *au pair* girl was a source of great excitement to me. One night, when she was putting up the black-out curtains in my aunt's bedroom, I slipped behind her and tickled her around the waist.

She fell on the floor in fits of laughter – and I seized my opportunity: I pressed my lips to her laughing mouth.

I don't think I heard bells ring, but I do know that the room spun round and I felt as though I was going to hit the ceiling. Fortunately, she didn't slap my face. In fact, she came back for more on a fairly regular basis.

Derek and Ellen Jameson

Blame the Sex Pistols. They brought us together by prompting our first row.

The punk rockers caused a sensation on a tea-time magazine programme by swearing and forcing the interviewer, Bill Grundy, to evacuate the studio.

As managing director of the *Daily Mirror*, Derek splashed the story across the front page: SEX PISTOLS IN FOUR-LETTER TV SHOCKER.

Being a feature writer myself, Ellen says, I lost no time in giving him my opinion when we met for the first time that evening. It was at a party for John Pemrose, husband of BBC TV's Anne Robinson.

'That's not a *Daily Mirror* front-page story,' I told him without waiting for an introduction. 'It was rubbish.'

'Don't tell me what to put on the front page, my girl,' he fired back. 'I was running a newspaper when you were still in nappies.'

We were locked in battle, staring into each other's eyes. From that moment on we just CLICked.

That was back in 1976, and we've been together ever since. We married in Arundel Cathedral in 1988.

Now, of course, we host a nightly chat show on BBC Radio 2.

As listeners know, the sparks are still flying!

Martin Jarvis

All actors yearn to play Hamlet.

My chance came in the mid-1970s for the Festival of British Theatre, at the beautiful Theatre Royal, Windsor. Such is the power of the role that I was told by the management I could choose my own director and so, at my suggestion, the splendid Martin Jenkins was awarded the job. Even better, I could also nominate the actress I would like to play opposite me as Ophelia. Wow!

I was a bit depressed when Mia Farrow turned down the opportunity to work with me – there's no accounting for taste …! But then I suggested another actress I was keen on. She was very well known and particularly current on TV at that time. She had, in fact, called me and, rather flatteringly I thought, pleaded for the part.

Mad about her as I was, I told her she was perfect for the 'mad' Ophelia. No problem, I assured her smugly. I'd just tell the director and that, as Shakespeare might have said, would be that …

But what do you think? My friend Martin Jenkins said, 'To be, or not to be? Definitely *not* to be. Oh, no, she wouldn't be right at all.' And he added, 'I've just offered the part to a brilliant new actress, Rosalind Ayres.'

'Rosalind who?' I muttered in my ignorance. 'Oh, well, suit yourself. That's the last time I get *you* a directing engagement.'

So the lovely Rosalind Ayres played the fair Ophelia opposite my very moody Dane. One critic said of my performance: 'Jarvis's Prince

of Denmark may not be as great as Gielgud's but it has the merit of being fast – and occasionally funny.' Well, at least the audience were able to catch their last buses home with a smile on their faces.

Rosalind Ayres stole all the notices. Oh, and, incidentally, she also stole my heart. Within a year we were married. Still are. Thank goodness Mia Farrow turned me down. And I can barely remember the name of that other actress who was so 'mad' for the role.

'The rest,' as Shakespeare *did* actually say, 'is silence … '

Sue Johnston

In my youth I fell in love many, many times – or, at least, I thought I did. Only when I gave birth to my son did I realize what true, unconditional love meant. It was both frightening and joyful – the most wonderful feeling in the world. It still endures, even though severely tested through turbulent teenage years. It is also a selfless love. My son loves me fat or thin, lazy or active, in despair or happy. I've never found a love like that in a relationship with a man. I live in hope!

Diane Louise Jordan

This untitled poem by E. Harris was given to me
by somebody very special. It contains the essence
of love, in beautiful images that compose a story.
I find hope in the poem among all the bleakness
of our contemporary
society. The dreams
that we all lose
for one reason or
another never die.

Between the ocean and the sea
There is a season we could call Hope of Love
Where all dreams that have fallen from our
    minds' branches
Endlessly float like Autumn leaves of Summer
    departure.
One old man and his true friend

With faces creased from a thousand years of
    children's laughter
Cast their net with breeze of grace.
Maybe his strong back now fades with age
For every net he hauls in seems much heavier.

As the catch of dreams spills into the bottom of
    their boat
He and his friend look into each other's eyes and
    smile.
They both hear the most beautiful misplaced
    notes of
Children's piano playing.
They both see the visions of practising actors
    and expectant mothers.
They both feel the touch, and taste the food
    shared by loving couples.
Look.
His friend points to the child's hands cupped as
    if an empty vessel waiting to receive.
Look at what our protective father gave.
He wonders: is her face moist from the warm
    sea spray
Or moist from the tears when she sees our
    reflection?

The crystal tide starts whispering to her
    favoured kind
Lapping at his fingers that he trails in her
    healing balm.
He sees the gifts that we have cast aside
Blood grey figures of life that died through our
    uncompromising progress.
Silently screaming, their long stained shadowed
    limbs
Reach to grasp any vessel
    trying, trying to bridge history.
Thinking they could save the child extinct
Virtual reality of maturing ritual in video
    arcade.
But not realistic enough for Nature's food
The water they drink is poisoned with our own
    waste.

A thousand years of rolled stone beat the cry
'Cull your dreams.'
Chanting, screaming against wooden hull, as
    they pull the boat from swell's reach.
Soon dawn will break and first light will strike
Upon market place display.
It is tradition here in the land we did not choose
    into whom is born

For poets and artists to haggle with promises of
    pictures and writing.
Haggling for your abandoned dreams.
They feed on your inspiration, for your hopes
    were true above all.
But now you sit building your grave.
These precious thoughts they will re-colour with
    bright children's crayon
Or write words that create a new spring.

The season that follows finds our two friends
Planting the new coloured seed along cliff edge.
It grows into past flower of dandelion
Where you pick its fruit from the breeze.
He will stand and look at his soul
Her clothes made of the simplest white and
    black linen
That reflect all he knows and shares in one
    fragile shell.

Neil Kinnock

....

It was 2 October 1962. It was the first week of my second year at university, and, among other things, I was busily engaged in recruiting new members for the student Socialist Society.

At lunchtime I was chatting my way through the Students' Union cafeteria queue when I came upon a group of girls who were obviously enjoying their first days at university. I remember one with stunning brown hair, skin like a peach, sparkling eyes and a laugh like a silver bell.

When she said, 'Are you the man from the Socialist Society I've been looking for? I want to join,' I was *smitten*. And I've stayed smitten for thirty-two years since.

She, I have to say, didn't CLICk quite as quickly. To be sure, she did come to the dance with me on the following Saturday – and she married me six years later. But there have been a few interesting clanks between the CLICks in the intervening time.

That's love, I guess …

Martyn Lewis

One evening back in 1968, a few months after I had landed my first real reporting job for HTV in Cardiff, I invited a young lady to see a much acclaimed theatre production in Bristol. We'd already had a few dates, and I was absolutely besotted with her. I decided that no expense would be spared and that I would treat her to a romantic candlelit dinner afterwards. Such was my precarious financial position at the time that I had to negotiate an overdraft with my bank manager to pay for the evening. The cash was duly withdrawn and the restaurant booked.

The play was hugely enjoyable, we were having great fun – but as we got into my car to head off to the restaurant, something made me check my pocket. I realized to my horror that I had left the extra money in my digs back in Cardiff. I racked my brains for a positive solution (I didn't have a

credit card in
those days)
and decided
to plump for
the only meal I
could afford – a
packet of fish and chips
and a bottle of lemonade. We duly consumed this
repast sitting on a wall overlooking the lights of
the Severn Bridge.

It was a warm, clear night. The setting – if you
only looked towards the bridge and the estuary –
was quite romantic. I must have had a rush of
blood to the head because, despite the less than
perfect circumstances, I decided to propose to her
there and then. Not surprisingly, she turned me
down. After that you might have thought there
was no hope for our relationship, but a few

months later, in rather better circumstances and surroundings, she said yes.

That young lady has been my wife for almost twenty-five years. My advice to would-be suitors is that even if you are turned down, a first proposal over fish and chips is not to be sniffed at!

Ian McCaskill

My Lesley died suddenly two years ago, after nine years of coping well with cancer – possibly the best nine years of our marriage. The kids and I slept, hugged and cried for two nights in Lesley's bed, then went out to buy a chain for her wedding ring. It suits me and should, like garlic, deter vampires.

I was fifty-four and very busy and could only helplessly observe my daughters' rage at their loss. Everyone was lovely to us. Except the ones who said it was for the best. No, it wasn't. Why are the survival rates in other

countries
higher than
ours? Can't
all be down to
duff statistics. I've always enjoyed the company of
women – especially women's women (much more
than men's), and I missed Lesley like stink. Still
do, of course.

A year or so later Pat, a family friend of thirty
years' standing, came for the weekend. She herself was cruelly widowed some years ago: Alan
died at forty-nine, at the height of his powers,
from a hereditary disease which gave Pat and her
delightful sons not a moment's warning. Their
anger and dismay are still just below the surface.

The rest, of course, is history now! Pat and I had a magical day at Leeds Castle. A kind couple even sent a surprise picture of the two of us, middle-aged but showing the body language of moon-struck teenagers. In the evening we all went to see Branagh and gang in *Much Ado* … We both (it transpired) ached to hold hands. But didn't. At night, though, we fell into each other's arms. We still consider it a miracle. I flew to Leeds the following weekend and now consider the 200 miles as nought. We meet often, do all the things young lovers do and have the phone bills to prove it! I am happier now than I have any right to be, and thank God for it. One day I may even take down the last of the silver wedding decorations.

Paul McKenna

....

About one week after I met my fiancée Clare she
had a dream. In the dream she and I were float-
ing above the earth as balls of light, then we
turned into 'beings'. Clare didn't want to go
down to the earth and was very worried, as she
felt it was a dangerous place, but I wanted to go,
as I felt there was important work there. She said,
'But how will I find you? How
will I know you when I do
find you?' I said, 'We'll
have a mark,' and I
touched her back,
and she touched
mine as I sped off
towards earth.

She related
this dream to me

and we both
discussed how
bizarre and
unusual it was
and tried to figure
out what it might mean. It

wasn't until months later that we remembered
the dream and to our astonishment realized that
we both had very similar, quite large, brown
patches on our backs, like birth marks. It is not
something we have ever told anyone, as it sounds
so strange, but we like to think it means we are
meant for each other.

Clive Mantle

From the first tender kiss
To the last long farewell,
There's a love deep inside us
Which no one can quell.

It's the joy in the spirit,
In our present and past,
For the greatest of loves
Is the Love that lasts.

Denis Norden

....

The line that came most immediately to mind on this subject was the one uttered by Danny de Vito, when he was playing a resident character in the American comedy series *Taxi*.

Talking of how he met his girlfriend, he said, 'There she was, dejected, desperate and stoned. Everything I could hope for in a woman … '

....

'Look,' she said – well, hissed really, all gritted teeth and narrowed eyes – as I hovered by the bedside, 'don't just stand there flapping about. Do something. This is all your bloody fault.' Then she uttered a stifled moan, grabbed my hand with a grip like a nutcracker and dug her nails into my skin.

'Push,' said the midwife, encouragingly.

'I am bloody pushing,' she said. 'What the hell do you think I'm doing here? And where's that gas and air? God, I hate men.'

The midwife moved in for a closer examination. 'Go downstairs and boil some water,' she said.

'Who, me?' I had assumed, in my usual quick-witted way, that she was talking to me, Diana, my

wife, hardly being in any condition to go downstairs and boil water. 'What for? You don't want a
cup of tea, do you?' I said to Diana.

'Do I look
like I want
a cup of
bloody
tea?' she
said, still
hissing.
'Aaargh!'

The midwife
straightened up. 'Go
downstairs,' she said, loudly and firmly, 'and boil
some water. Never mind what for. Lots of water.'

So I did. I boiled water in kettles. I boiled water
in saucepans. You could have had a bath in the
amount of water I boiled, and I might have saved
myself the bother because none of it was ever
used, or even asked for.

I was scrabbling about in a cupboard looking for
one more receptacle in which water might be

boiled when the midwife called to me. 'All right, you can come back.'

So I did and now, miraculously, there were four of us in the bedroom – Diana and me, the midwife and my daughter Samantha, the only one of us who hadn't come in through the door. She was scrunched up and purplish, damp and yelling lustily and still attached by the umbilical cord. She was also the most beautiful thing I had ever seen, and I hated the midwife for sending me off to boil all that water and denying me the privilege of witnessing my firstborn's entry into the world.

Fourteen months later – same bedroom, different midwife – we went through it all again. It was still my bloody fault, Diana still hated men (a fact which, happily, she had obviously forgotten in the

interim) and there was again this apparent and urgent need for vast quantities of boiled water.

But I was an old hand now, and this time I stood my ground. 'We don't need boiled water,' I said. 'We didn't need it last time and we don't need it now. I'm staying here.'

And I did. I stayed and watched the birth of Emma, our second daughter, and when it was over and she was in her mother's arms I realized that tears had been streaming, hitherto unnoticed, down my face and yet I was smiling like a fool.

I leant across and touched the dark, wet curls on my daughter's head and for the second time in fourteen months I experienced love at first sight. Oh, when I was younger, of course, I had known that sensation many times. At seventeen, eighteen and nineteen I'd fallen in love at first sight more often than I can remember. But somehow it never lasted, and sometimes it even died at second sight.

This time, though, it was different, just as it had been when Samantha was born. This was a love at first sight that was never going to fade, that was indeed only going to grow. And so it has turned out.

Nick Owen

I somehow knew that it was my day of destiny. Aged fourteen and still very new to the world of romance, I was taking Susan out on my first-ever date. Susan's not her real name – it was actually Philippa – but I'm calling her Susan to protect her identity, which is what you do in these sorts of stories. My mate Paul and I were taking Olivia and Susan (real name Philippa, remember) to see the Elvis movie *Kid Galahad*. Typical crass Elvis film of the time, but I loved it because it's a landmark in Nick Owen's
Chronicle of
the Late
Twentieth
Century.

I was a shade
tentative about
the first nervous

approach, but Paul and Olivia were a terrific support as I plucked up the courage to land a smacker on Philippa's cherry-reds. I think Elvis had just launched into his little-known classic 'King of the Whole Wide World' when I leaned over and made the first foray. Wow! It was like being plugged into the national grid: what an unforgettable experience. I'd never felt up to much with the girls (I was so ugly as a baby that my parents fed me with a catapult).

We went strong for some time, then I started going out with her best friend – what a cad. But, Philippa, wherever you are these days, thanks for the memory!

Peter Polycarpou

Deborah tells
this story that
when she was
attending a 'Save
the Tower'
charity dinner
at All Hallows-
by-the-Tower
she opened the
programme and
saw my photo.
Apparently she
liked what she
saw and rather let her

imagination run away with her, thinking, 'I wouldn't mind taking him home!' At any rate, there were a number of very fine singers on the bill that evening, and among them was the then Phantom of the Opera, Dave Willetts. While

enjoying his singing voice, she had no amorous feeling towards his photo …

Now we cut to a year later when Deborah has been invited to a performance of *Phantom* at Her Majesty's Theatre by a very dear friend of mine, and she's having dinner with the Phantom himself after the show. Deborah only changed her mind about going at the very last minute. Well, as the lights were dimming she realized she hadn't got a good look at the photo of the actor playing Phantom. In fact, she thought it was Dave Willetts again.

Imagine her surprise when she opened the programme as the lights slowly faded and she saw my face again! I was playing Phantom, and at dinner afterwards we had our first story to tell others. We've been together more or less ever since.

Jonathan Pryce

....

Twenty-two years ago I met, and fell in love with, the actress Katy Fahy. We have been together ever since.

When all alone
and hope is gone
I think of Kate
With nothing on.

(With apologies to
my friend the poet
Adrian Mitchell!)

Esther Rantzen

One of the many reasons why I have never been able to rub shoulders with sophisticated café society is that I get extremely hungry around half past six at night. When I have to work late in the office (it happens quite often) I can ward off starvation with BBC canteen egg-and-chips. But when I rush from the office to the theatre, the first act is normally punctuated by terrible stomach rumbles from Rantzen.

When Desmond Wilcox first took me to the theatre he put up with these dreadful glugs and rumbles without complaint, although every now and again the row in front would turn round and shush at me. But early on in our acquaintance, in the first interval of a very serious drama, he excused himself when we went to the bar and disappeared completely. He arrived back with a greaseproof parcel in his hand. I unwrapped it and found the most delectable hot salt-beef sandwich, with just the right amount of mustard, which he had dashed to Soho to buy for me. We were surrounded by American ladies in mink coats who sighed with envy when they saw it. One of them looked at Desmond and said, 'What a man!'

I have never forgotten that moment, when true sophisticates of the London theatre-going audience fell in love with my husband-to-be, and so did I. The fragrance of a salt-beef sandwich still brings romantic stars to my eyes.

Amanda Redington

I was fourteen years old and head-over-heels in love with Angus Patterson. He seemed oblivious to my love and over a period of four months said only two words to me, 'Excuse me', as he pushed passed me in the cafeteria!

I analysed those two words for days. What was he trying to tell me? After all, he didn't have to say anything. He could have just pushed past.

Then one day in class I heard whispers of 'Pass it on'. I looked up to see Angus at the other side of the room smiling at me, and before I knew it the boy sitting next to me had shoved a great big green rubber in my hand with 'AP loves AR' written on it in thick black felt pen. It only took a few seconds for it to sink in: at last Angus was declaring his love for me. I just couldn't believe my luck.

I immediately turned the rubber over and wrote, 'The feeling's mutual,' and, blushing furiously, passed the rubber back to him, gave him my best smile and swooned through the rest of the lesson.

It was only after class that I discovered that Angus had been going out with Angela Reece for a whole week and the rubber was supposed to be passed on to her. I'm not sure I ever lived it down.

Gary Rhodes

....

My Jennifer

I was standing on the platform
waiting for a train.
It was cold, wet and windy
Just pouring down with rain.

94

Then she came along
and my sun began to shine.
She had beautiful long dark hair
And I knew she had to be mine.

We took our train journey
And didn't even speak:
Little did I know
We were to meet the following week.

I started at catering college
to learn how to cook.
She started at the same time:
It was straight from a romance book.

We stayed there for three years
And didn't really get on
Until towards the end,
Then we really started to bond.

We've been together ever since
About fifteen years,
Working through the industry
With blood, sweat and tears.

We only married five years ago –
We just had to be sure.
Since then we've had two kids:
Samuel's six and George is four.

My wife's name is Jennifer,
And I love her with all my heart,
But I'm not sure if it's me she loves
or my glazed lemon tart!

Paul Ross

The night I
realized my
wife, Kerry,
was the perfect
woman for me
was when we
were holding
hands over a
candlelit dinner.
I tugged her towards

me for a between-courses kiss, and her fringe
caught fire. Without blinking or bawling she
pulled away from my lips, doused her fringe in a
glass of water, then came back for the second half
of the snog.

Red-hot and cool – the perfect combination!

Jimmy Savile

I have CLICked 8,482,641 times. I intended to get married 8,482,640 times.

This is because of my dance-hall and disco life: I fell in love with all the girls I met – and still do.

All this and running 205 marathons as well. Wow!

Carol Smillie

Remembering the first time I saw Alex is easy. He was modelling in a fashion show, and I was unashamedly drooling! Apparently the feeling was mutual, as I discovered when he'd blagged his way on to a photo shoot with me. No, he wasn't modelling this time: he was holding the lights! A month or so later we had our first dinner date, and in less than a year we were married.

But if I had to pinpoint the moment when I really knew he was the man for me, it would have to be after a bad bout of gastro-enteritis. I had it, and he smiled all the way through it, even though I looked like Methuselah's granny. What a trooper! I wonder if he'd do that now …

Peter Snow

I had been dispatched by ITN to report on the Commonwealth Conference in Ottawa in the summer of 1973. It's an unromantic place – all grey stone and featureless, pine-clad hills. But it was to change my life.

First call for a visiting journalist was the Media Supervisor's office. I expected an obstructive bureaucrat. What I got was a hazel-eyed blonde with hair down below her shoulders and a smile that, more than twenty years later, still sweeps all before it, as it did that first afternoon. I do not remember much about the conference, except that whenever I could find an excuse I was discussing administrative details with the Media Supervisor, and there was often so *much* detail that we had to work on it through lunch and deep into the evening and even into the small hours.

When the Commonwealth went home, I stayed on. Ann and I went canoeing in Algonquin Park and spent three enchanted days at a lodge where you could see nothing but lakes and forest. I am normally a very responsible fellow, but when I turned up at the airport to fly back home to my job in London, I could not board the aircraft. Some second sense told me that if I did not go back to Ann in Ottawa, I would not see her again. One of those defining moments.

I pleaded some lame excuse to ITN, seized my suitcase off the aeroplane and taxied back to Ann. We had fallen in love long before the next week was up, and we were married two years later.

Chris Tarrant

I used to know this lovely gypsy lady down in Devon. She was a real old rogue but incredibly wise, and I used to sit in her kitchen drinking home-made soup while she chatted on to me for hours about everything under the sun.

She made a living out of selling things to people on their doorsteps:
brushes, brooches,
lucky charms,
the lot. The
old rubbish
she managed
to talk people
into buying
used to
amaze me.
She reckoned

that, in the main, people tended to buy some-thing just to get rid of her, and I'm sure she was absolutely right. She used to be loudly abusive to people who didn't cough up, and rather than have the whole neighbourhood peeping round the curtains as this loud-mouthed Romany slagged you off as a meanie, most people would give in, if only to get her off the doorstep.

She told me very proudly that she was travelling through Scotland once, and in the course of a week she sold eleven cases of lucky heather ...

She certainly knew a lot about people. She's been married for something like forty-five years, and she was always counselling me about my con-fused, and mainly disastrous, love life. At the age of nineteen I used to wake up in the morning, fall madly in love by lunchtime and be fed up with the whole thing by about seven o'clock in the evening.

I'd lived briefly with a couple of girls in London, and been absolutely potty about two or three others, but it always seemed to go wrong somehow. They'd take exception to some little habit of mine, like bringing other girls back home from the pub or keeping maggots under the bed, and it would all break up in bitterness and confusion.

What always struck me, and saddened me, really, was how little it all actually mattered in the end. A couple of times when my romances had broken down, for whatever reason, I'd been absolutely shattered. I'd gone out on monumental binges that had lasted for days and then dripped about like a wet lettuce for weeks. I'd been sure my whole world had come apart at the seams. There was no possible point in going on. I'd never ever look at another, I'd become a monk, I'd join the

Foreign Legion, I'd get an allotment … and then one day I'd walk into somewhere like the local chippy and there behind the counter would be some raven-haired beauty with a huge chest and a smell of vinegar, and the whole silly business would start all over again.

I was chuntering on about the impermanence of everything one night in old Peggy's kitchen, and she, of course, understood the whole problem. 'You're only here once, and in the end none of it matters a damn. It all comes out in the wash … ' And then she told me a very simple story that somehow put it all in a nutshell.

Long before she'd met her husband she'd fallen madly in love with a much older man, who was married with three kids. She had gone through absolute hell over this bloke for four years, sure that one day he'd leave his wife and marry her, but, of course, he didn't, and one night he'd told her it was all over. She was absolutely distraught, suicidal even. And, sobbing hysterically, she'd gone up to one of the cliffs high above Torbay and just stood there in the wind, closing her eyes and willing herself to jump off.

Several times she'd looked down at the rocks and the raging sea, hundreds of feet below, and all but summoned up the courage to let herself go, but each time she just couldn't quite will herself out into space. In the end she'd somehow dragged herself away from the cliff's edge and gone home sadly to begin an empty life.

'And d'you know?' she says, 'I was thinking about him the other day, and I can't even remember his bloody name!'

Anthea Turner

Before Peter and I got married
we were invited to a little pre-
wedding chat (tea and biscuits)
with the vicar, Basil Peel. He is
a delightful man, now retired
and living in Wales.

While the open fire crackled away, he gave us one
piece of advice that has always stayed with me:
never let the sun go down on your wrath.

I'm happy to say that it has rarely needed to be
used, but what a valuable collection of words.

Michael van Wijk ('Wolf')

Paula, my girlfriend, and I knew each other just to say hello to for many years. Only after we got together later on did we discover that we were both crazy about each other, but neither of us ever let on when we met.

I accidentally bumped into Paula one night when she was leaving the bank where she worked. I had just left my solicitor's, which was across the road from her bank. I said

hello, and we
made small
talk about
nothing
for over
an hour
before I
finally
asked her

if she would like to get together for a drink one day. We eventually arranged it for a week later and exchanged phone numbers.

During the following week Paula and I spoke to each other on the telephone every night, and we have been inseparable ever since. That was almost three years ago.

Ruby Wax

....

I used to calculate carefully: will this man at some point stop returning my calls and never speak to me again without an explanation? This is more or less how I'd find my man in the past. In other words, they were all lethal. When I first spotted my husband, Ed, I thought, 'No way. He's too tall and too nice.' It was during the rehearsals of *Girls on Top* (he was the director) that I broke my habit of a lifetime and went for the good guy – not because I was suddenly cured of my endless stream of bastards but because he was the only man in the rehearsal rooms. And so, due to lack of choice, he became the object of my desire.

James Whale

It was in London's
West End on a
not-so-cold
night in
December
1968. I had
been invited
to a dance by
my schoolfriend
David Stephenson
(in fact, I haven't
seen him since).
David was studying hairdressing at the London
College of Fashion, just off Oxford Circus, and
Chicken Shack were playing.

I was waiting outside for a girl I'd met in Camden
Town the night before. I was wearing my new
jacket – my pride and joy. It was made of antique

leather and had studs, and very trendy it was too. Anyway, I waited and waited for the girl to show, but she never did, so I went into the dance. I couldn't find anyone I knew and decided to call it a night.

On my way out I saw this stunning girl in a completely backless catsuit: I asked her for a dance, then offered her a drink – and she said OK.

As we were leaving, we went to collect my lovely leather jacket from the cloakroom. It was the end of the evening, and every coat, including mine, had gone. I think she felt sorry for me because she bought the drinks at the pub round the corner.

I never got my jacket back, but Melinda and I are still together, two children and twenty-five years later!

Victoria Wood

I fell in love with a twin in Bury Baths when I was ten. I kissed him, but as it was under the water and I didn't have my glasses on, I've never been sure which one it was.